How to use this

Leap Ahead Workpad: English
your child as they learn key ski
The activities are based on the national curriculum
and have a number of features to help both parent
and child get the most out of home learning.

Clear and
simple
instructions

Lots of
activities
keep
children
engaged

Sounds All Around

Look at each picture. What sound does it make?
Can you make the sound LOUDLY and quietly?

z z ^{z}

4

Clear,
uncluttered
layout,
suitable
for young
learners

Activity
answers
available

1

Flip the pages

Follow the
page numbers
and flip the
book around
as you work
through the
activities.

Follow the
page numbers
and flip the
book around
as you work
through the
activities.

This is Me!

Draw a picture of yourself:

Write your name:

Sounds All Around

Look at each picture. What sound does it make?
Can you make the sound LOUDLY and quietly?

Shadow Pairs

Look carefully at the shapes to see which ones match. Draw a line between each pair.

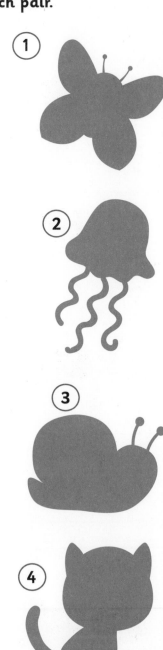

a

b

c

d

1

2

3

4

Answers on page 29

5

Animal Patterns

Look carefully at these animal pairs and circle the odd one out in each row.

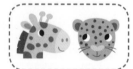  

Answers on page 29

It's Time to Rhyme!

Look at the pictures in each row and say the words out loud. Then colour in the last rhyming picture in each row.

frog   log   dog

cat   bat   hat

boat   coat   goat

It's Time to Rhyme!

Look at the pictures in each row and say the words out loud. Then colour in the last rhyming picture in each row.

wig

dig

pig

sting

sing

wing

ham

lamb

jam

claw

saw

paw

Over the Moon

Follow the arrows to draw around these planets.

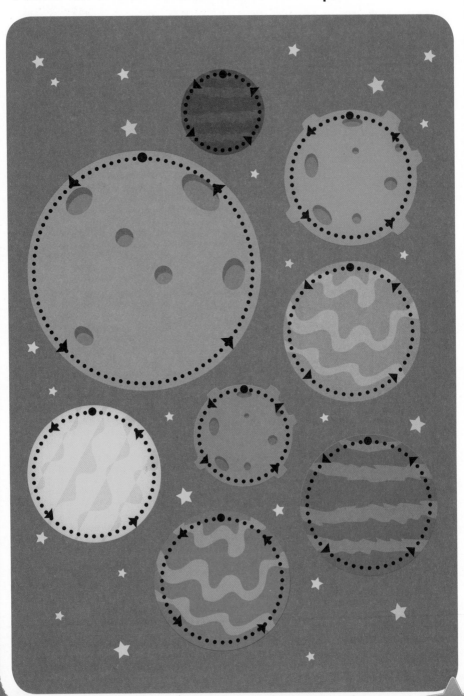

Monkey Message

Monty Monkey has been learning about letters. Help him by following the arrows to make these letter shapes.

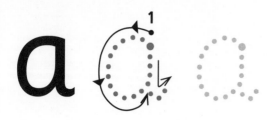

a

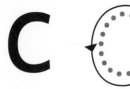

c

e

o

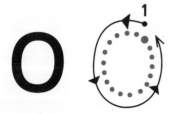

Odd Rhyme Out

Look at the pictures in each row and say the words out loud. Colour the two words that rhyme in blue. Colour the word that doesn't rhyme in green. The first one has been done for you below.

Example:

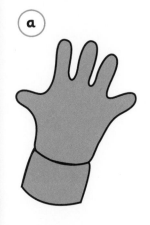 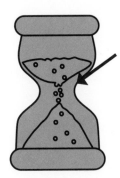 

hand   sand   sheep

b

duck   moon   spoon

Odd Rhyme Out

Look at the pictures in each row and say the words out loud. Colour the two words that rhyme in blue. Colour the word that doesn't rhyme in green.

(c)

flag   coat   bag

(d)

sock   jumper   clock

(e)

hat   bat   pig

Farmer Fred's Fence

Follow the arrows and finish the fence to help Farmer Fred.

Now follow the arrows to practise writing these letters.

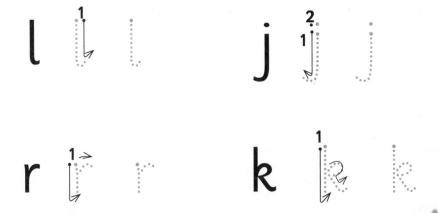

'a' and 's' Words

Colour the items that start with 'a' in green.
Colour the items that start with 's' in blue.
Two items have been coloured for you.

sock

sunglasses

carrot

robot

duck

ant

arrow

cat

cow

apple

chair

sack

Answers on page 29

Ocean I Spy

Play I Spy with this ocean scene and see how many items you can spot. For example, "I spy with my little eye, something beginning with... w."

All at Sea

It's a nice day out at sea. Follow the arrows to draw some waves around the fishing boat.

Now follow the arrows to practise writing these letters.

't' and 'p' Words

Colour the items that start with 't' in green.
Colour the items that start with 'p' in blue.
Two items have been coloured for you.

penguin

pen

glove

bed

t

dog

train

p

tent

ring

bird

sock

10

ten

pig

Same Sounds

Look at the pictures and say the words out loud. Draw a circle around the picture with the same beginning sound as the rest of the things in each row. The first one has been done for you.

a

sock

sack

1 ant

2 sand

b

tap

ten

3 toe

4 goat

c

nest

neck

5 duck

6 net

Answers on page 29

18

Lily Pad Letters

Look at these happy frogs. Follow the arrows to draw the shape they make as they hop from one lily pad to the next.

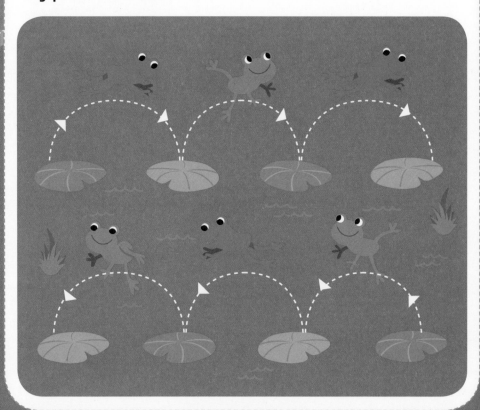

Now follow the arrows to practise writing these letters.

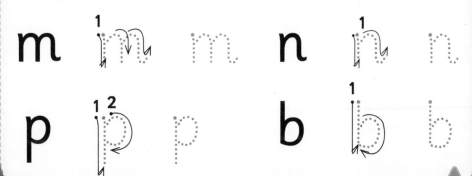

'n' and 'm' Words

Colour the items that start with 'n' in green.
Colour the items that start with 'm' in blue.
Two items have been coloured for you.

monster

net

boat

mug

neck

n

peg

fish

m

foot

man

girl

pins

Answers on page 30

Odd Toy Out

These toys have letters on them, but the odd letters out keep getting in the way! Circle the odd letter out in each row.

a) s s s t s

b) m n m m m

c) o p p p p

d) g g r g g

Answers on page 30

Silly Sentences

Read the beginning of each silly sentence out loud.
What silly word will you put at the end?
Use the pictures to help.

Simon Sailor's sack is full of ....

snails   slugs   sand

Wispy Witch wishes for a ....

walrus   wasp   wand

Millie Mouse makes a mess with ....

mittens   mud   moles

Billie Baker bakes ....

biscuits   bugs   beds

Zigzag Robots

Sammy Science has almost finished his robots.
Help him to complete them by following the
zigzag lines.

Now follow the arrows to practise writing
these letters.

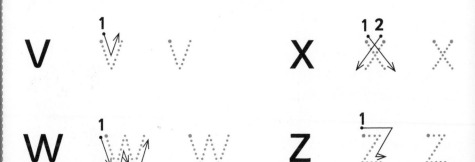

V   V   V

X   X   X

W   W   W

Z   Z   Z

23

'd' and 'g' Words

Colour the items that start with 'd' in green.
Colour the items that start with 'g' in blue.
Two items have been coloured for you.

dragon

hat

heart

gate

garden

d

goat

rabbit

g

cap

bed

dog

duck

star

Answers on page 30

24

Rhyming I Spy

Look at the park scene and use these pictures to play Rhyming I Spy. For example, "I spy with my little eye, something that rhymes with... balloon."

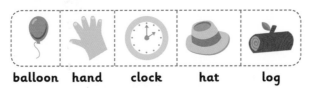

balloon   hand   clock   hat   log

What's the Picture?

There's a shape hidden in the grid below. Colour the 'c' squares red and the 'k' squares yellow to find out what it is.

k	c	c	c	k	c	c	c	k
c	c	c	c	c	c	c	c	c
k	c	c	c	c	c	c	c	k
k	k	c	c	c	c	c	k	k
k	k	k	c	c	c	k	k	k
k	k	k	k	c	k	k	k	k
k	k	k	k	k	k	k	k	k

Answer on page 30

Aladdin's Magic Lamp

How many things in the cave can you find beginning with each of these sounds?

| b | h | f | r |

Hidden in the cave is Aladdin's magic lamp. When you find it, draw a circle around it.

27

Me and My Sounds

What letter does your name start with?

....

Draw a picture of something that starts with the same sound as your name:

Draw a picture of you and your best friend:

Answers

Page 5: Shadow Pairs
a – 3, b – 4, c – 2, d – 1

Page 6: Animal Patterns

Page 14: 'a' and 's' Words
'a': arrow, apple, ant
's': sunglasses, sock, sack

Page 17: 't' and 'p' Words
't': ten, tent, train,
'p': pen, penguin, pig

Page 18: Same Sounds

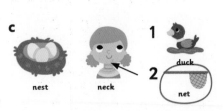

a

sock   sack   ant

sand

b

tap   ten   toe

goat

c

nest   neck   duck

net

Answers

Page 20: 'n' and 'm' Words
'n': net, neck
'm': man, monster, mug

Page 21: Odd Toy Out

 a t

 b n

 c o

 d r

Page 24: 'd' and 'g' Words
'd': dog, dragon, duck
'g': garden, goat, gate

Page 26: What's the Picture?
A heart

k	c	c	c	k	c	c	c	k
c	c	c	c	c	c	c	c	c
k	c	c	c	c	c	c	c	k
k	k	c	c	c	c	c	k	k
k	k	k	c	c	c	k	k	k
k	k	k	k	c	k	k	k	k
k	k	k	k	k	k	k	k	k

Rhyming Time

Draw a line between each pair of rhyming words.
The first pair is done for you.

a pin   tip 1

b sat   tan 2

c tap   tin 3

d pan   pat 4

                    5

e nip   nap

Listen and Draw

Listen carefully to a grown-up as they read these instructions. Draw a picture of what they describe in the space below.

Instructions:
Put the sun at the top.
Draw one tree on each side of the picture.
Give each tree five branches.
Draw a bird in the tree on the right of the picture.
Draw some flowers on the grass.
Colour in the picture.

Animal Antics

Look at the animals. What do you think they are doing?
Find the correct word from the box for each picture.

act | hop | hit | pat | sit | pick

(a)

....

(b)

....

(c)

....

(d)

....

(e)

....

(f)

....

Answers on page 51

Party Letters

Fill in the missing letters in the correct order and complete the alphabet.

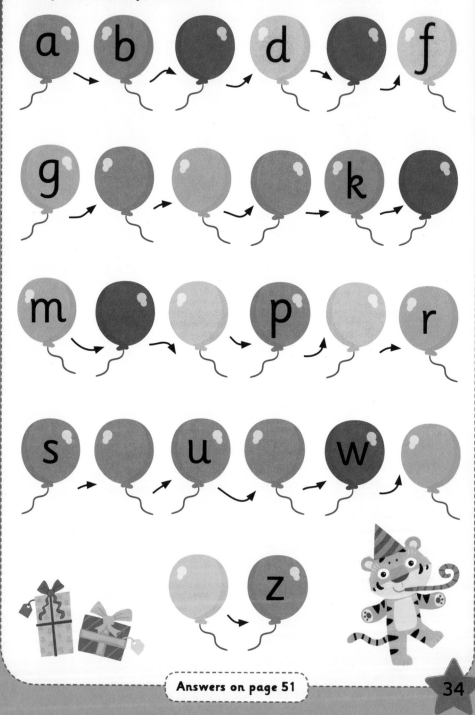

a   b   ___   d   ___   f

g   ___   ___   ___   k   ___

m   ___   ___   p   ___   r

s   ___   u   ___   w   ___

___   z

What's the First Letter?

Practise writing these letters:

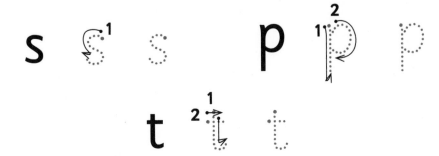

Look at each picture, read the word out loud and choose
a letter from the box to fill in the missing first letter.
The first one has been done for you.

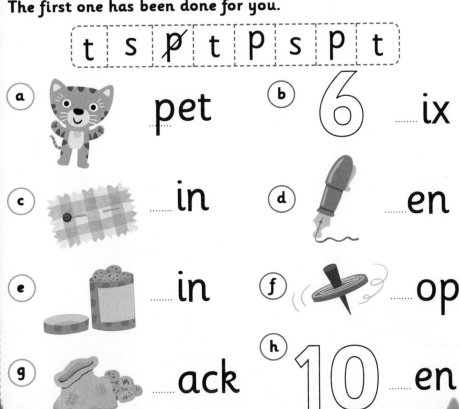

| t | s | p̶ | t | p | s | p | t |

a) _p_et

b) 6 ___ix

c) ___in

d) ___en

e) ___in

f) ___op

g) ___ack

h) 10 ___en

Word Wheel

Look at each picture around the wheel and say what it is out loud. Then, write the letter that the word begins with in the space inside the wheel.

Zoo I Spy

Play Zoo I Spy in the scene below and take it in turns to ask and answer. How many things can you find beginning with these letters?

a	s	t	p	n	m	d	c

Sounds All Around

Say the sound that is above the dot in each word.
Then, say the whole word out loud.

man   kit    wet

fun    run    win

jog    lap   pig

cot   vet   bag

sad    ham   pet

What's in the Picture?

Colour in the picture using the code below to reveal a hidden image. What can you see?

k = █   j = ░   r = ▓

l = ▒   u = ▓   w = █

Answer on page 51

Mr Mouse's Rocket

Listen to the story. How do you think it should finish?
Write your own ending and draw it in the space.

Mr Mouse was hungry. "I need some
cheese," he said. He looked in the
cupboard, but it was empty.
So Mr Mouse went to the shops.

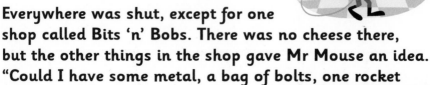

Everywhere was shut, except for one
shop called Bits 'n' Bobs. There was no cheese there,
but the other things in the shop gave Mr Mouse an idea.
"Could I have some metal, a bag of bolts, one rocket
engine and a small, round window,
please?" The shopkeeper came
back with a heavy bag of things.

Mr Mouse took the bag home.
All night he hammered and drilled.
Every now and then, he looked out the window
at the moon. Finally, Mr Mouse stopped and
looked at what he had made. It was an
amazing space rocket! Now he could fly to
the moon and bring back lots of cheese.
He climbed aboard and called out,
"10, 9, 8, 7, 6, 5, 4, 3, 2, 1... BLAST OFF!"

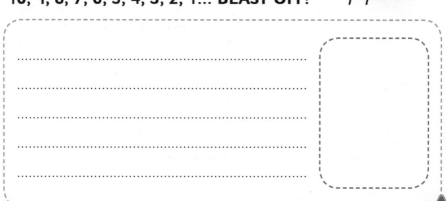

....

....

....

....

....

Little Words

Practise tracing the dotted words.
The first letter of each word has
arrows to help you get started.
Then write the words in the spaces.

Jack had a bug.   a

He put it in a box,

but the bug got out.

The bug was big.

It went up Mum's leg!

Mum said, "Get it off!"

Colour in the picture using the code to reveal a hidden image. What object can you see?

e = █   b = ▢   f = ▢

c = ▢   a = ▢   o = ▢

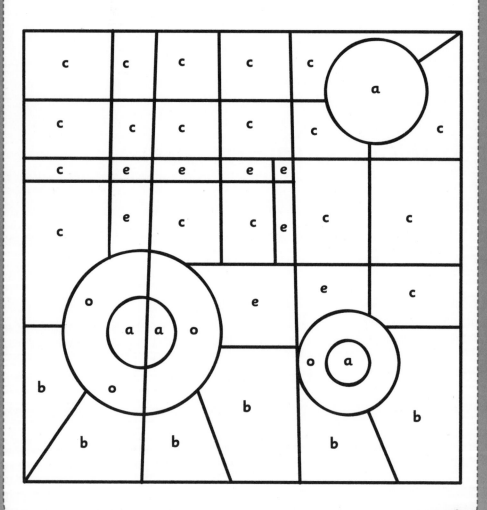

Answer on page 52

Cartoon Time

Read the captions under each box and draw pictures to match. Then, tell the story out loud.

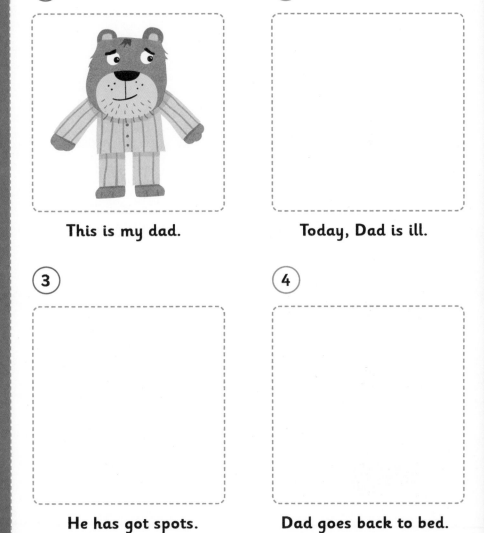

① This is my dad.

② Today, Dad is ill.

③ He has got spots.

④ Dad goes back to bed.

Missing Letters

Complete the words below using the correct letter from the box. The first one has been done for you.

| a | ø | m | g | e | r | f | d |

a  cot

ha b

c 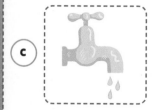 t_p

_ag  d

e  p_t

_in  f

g  lo_

sa_  h

Answers on page 52

Capitals and Full Stops

Circle each word that starts with a capital letter.

Jack   Sam   win

bat   pet

Tom

man

sit   Amy

A sentence starts with a capital letter and ends with a full stop, like this...

This is my book.

Add full stops and capital letters to these sentences.

......his is my pet......

...... am a girl......

...... like apples......

......y bag is big......

......here is a way......

Answers on page 52

Word Match

Look at the words and matching pictures in the grid below. Can you match them again by drawing a line between each pair? The first one has been done for you.

at	go	up	and
you	this	I	on

up

I

on

go

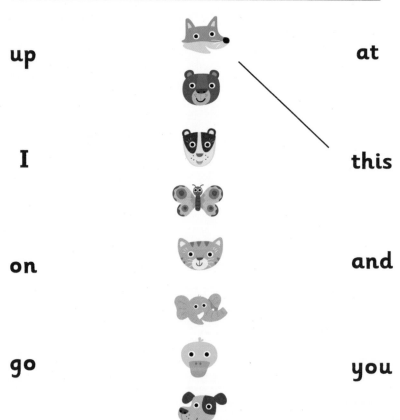

at

this

and

you

Everyday Words

Read each of these words and copy them in the spaces.

my	....	is	....
look	....	go	....
going	....	the	....
we	....	away	....
she	....	play	....
dog	....	and	....
like	....	look	....
said	....	of	....
was	....	went	....
day	....	come	....

Writing Captions

Look at each of the pictures below. Then, write what you see on the lines underneath. The first one has been done for you.

A pig on the bus.

Come to the Party!

Fill in the missing words on this party invitation.

To ....

Please come to my birthday party!

It is a .... party so please come

dressed as a ....

The date for the party is ....

It will start at .... and finish at ....

The address is ....

....

....

I really hope you can come.

From ....

My Dog

Use the pictures as clues to complete the end of each sentence. Two have already been done for you.

My dog is called Pat.

He chases _____ .

He chews old _____

and sleeps on a _____ .

Pat loves to run

and play in the _____ .

He is lots of _____ !

Answers on page 52

Answers

Page 31: Rhyming Time
a – 3, b – 4, c – 5, d – 2, e – 1

Page 33: Animal Antics
a – act, b – sit, c – hit,
d – hop, e – pick, f – pat

Page 34: Party Letters
a, b, c, d, e, f, g, h, i, j, k, l, m,
n, o, p, q, r, s, t, u, v, w, x, y, z

Page 35: What's the First Letter?
a – pet, b – six, c – pin, d – pen,
e – tin, f – top, g – sack, h – ten

Page 39: What's in the Picture?
A rocket

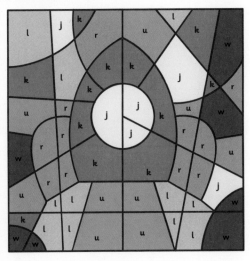

Page 41: Little Words
a, in, the, was, It, said

Answers

Page 42: What's in the Picture?
A tractor

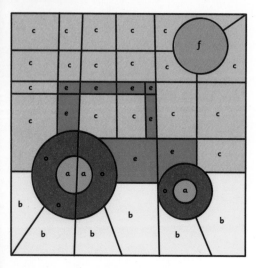

Page 44: Missing Letters
a – cot, b – ham,
c – tap, d – rag,
e – pet, f – fin,
g – log, h – sad

Page 45: Capitals and Full Stops
Jack, Sam, Tom, Amy
This is my pet.
I am a girl.
I like apples.
My bag is big.
There is a way.

Page 50: My Dog
My dog is called Pat. He chases cats.
He chews old hats and sleeps on a mat.
Pat loves to run and play in the sun.
He is lots of fun!